MR. TICKLE

and Friends
Sticker & Puzzle Fun

Roger Hargreaves

MR. MEN   LITTLE MISS

MR. MEN™ LITTLE MISS™ © THOIP (a SANRIO company)

Mr Tickle and Friends Sticker and Puzzle Fun © 2018 THOIP (a SANRIO company).
Printed and published under licence from Penguin Random House LLC
This edition published in Great Britain in 2018 by Dean,
an imprint of Egmont UK Limited
The Yellow Building, 1 Nicholas Road, London W11 4AN

ISBN 978 0 6035 7511 2
70040/001
Printed in Italy

How to Draw Mr Tickle

Step 1
Get started by ...
Drawing a simple round body.

Step 2
Next ...
Add feet, a big smile and eyes.

Step 3
And then ...
Colour him in orange and add his little blue hat.
And he's finished.

Step 4

Wait a minute ...
That doesn't look quite right.
Here's what Mr Tickle should really look like!

Draw your own Mr Tickle here. Then keep your eyes wide open for an unsuspecting someone to tickle!

Grab Your Spoons!

The Mr Men are holding their very own sports day!
The egg and spoon race kicks things off.

Use your stickers to add the Mr Men and their spoons to the race.
Who wins? Who loses? It's up to you!

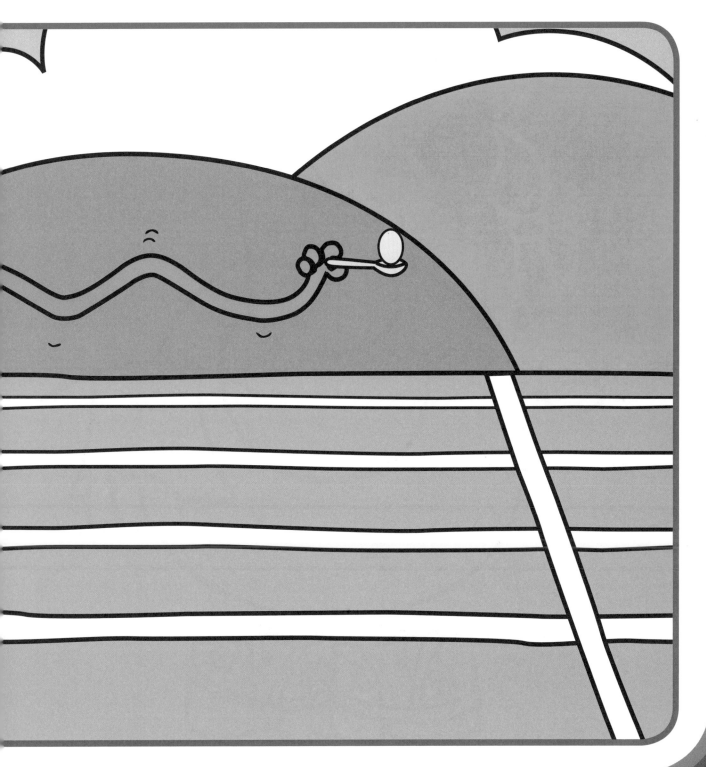

Silly Scribbles

Mr Silly is really very, VERY silly! He is using his paint pot as a hat and his hat as a paint pot! Using your yellow crayon, colour in Mr Silly.

Mr Tickle is very lucky to have such long arms! He can reach the prettiest flowers. Count the bees, then colour in the scene as neatly as you can.

Memory Game

Mr Clever has a challenge for you.
Look at the pictures on this page, then close the book
and see how many you can remember. No cheating!

How Many Hankies?

ATISHOO! Mr Sneeze needs lots of hankies! Count how many there are of each type and write the numbers in the boxes.

a b c

Who am I?

How well do you know the Mr Men? Would you be able to guess which Mr Men character you are with a few simple questions?
Now is your chance to find out!

You will need:

Mr Men character cards and sticky tape
OR sticky notes and pencils

How to play:

1. Choose one of the Mr Men character cards from the back of this book and tape it to your friend's back, making sure they don't see it. Or you can write the name of a Mr Men character on a sticky note instead if you like.

2. Your friend will do the same for you.

3. You now take it in turns to ask 'yes or no' questions to work out who you are. For example, "Do I wear a hat?", "Am I red?"

4. When you think you know who you are, simply make your guess and the first person to guess correctly wins the game!

Spot and Say

How good are you at finding people in a crowd? See if you can spot the Mr Men and Little Miss meeting these descriptions! Who else is hiding in the crowd?

Wearing glasses ☐

With a moustache ☐

Wearing a crown ☐

There are two of them ☐

With a red nose ☐

With orange, curly hair ☐

Wearing odd shoes ☐

Wearing a spotty hat ☐

Very tall ☐

Very small ☐

Answer: Walter the worm.

Tickle TV

What is Mr Tickle watching on TV?

Mr Lazy's Lazy Words

Zzzzzz. Time for a nap, Mr Lazy?
Can you find Mr Lazy's five favourite words in this grid?

d	w	s	t	l	y
r	b	i	n	a	o
e	g	t	h	z	p
a	m	a	k	y	b
m	l	c	m	y	e
s	l	e	e	p	d

bed

sleep

sit

dream

lazy

Colour Match

Use your pencil to draw lines to match the colours to the splats of paint.

blue

green

red

yellow

Answers: Mr Happy – red; Mr Jelly – green; Mr Messy – yellow; Mr Mischief – blue.

MR. TICKLE

MR. GREEDY

MR. HAPPY

MR. BUMP

MR. MESSY

MR. SMALL

MR. NOISY

MR. FUNNY

MR. STRONG